WELCOME TO ODDLEIGH

ODDLEIGH (pronounced ODD-LEE): A town with more than its fair share of strange happenings...

CONTENTS

OM NOM NOM

3

The Haunting of Lorringham

WELCOME TO ODDLEIGH

by

TOR FREEMAN

FOR JESSIE, OF COURSE!
BEST SISTER AND COMICS-PARTNER,
WHO GAVE ME SO MUCH HELP
WITH THIS BOOK! ♥

WELCOME TO ODDLEIGH

First published in Great Britain in 2018 by

Bog Eyed Books,
39 Coptefield Drive,
Belvedere,
Kent, DA17 5RL

Text and Illustrations © 2018 Tor Freeman

Printed and bound by comicprintinguk.com

Logo designed by baxterandbailey.co.uk

British Library Cataloguing in Publication Data:
a catalogue record for this book is available from the British Library

ISBN 978-0-9955553-6-5

MY TROUBLE BEGAN ABOUT A YEAR AGO, WITH THE DEATH OF MY GREAT-AUNT, GERTWIN.

WE WERE NEVER CLOSE— IN FACT I FELT SHE'D NEVER LIKED ME. BUT AS THE NEXT OF KIN, I RECEIVED HER TITLE, LADY ANGORA, AND... HER HOUSE— LORRINGHAM...

AN ANCIENT FAMILY HOME, LORRINGHAM... IN THE MIDDLE OF THE ODDLEIGH MOORS, THE PRIDE OF OUR FAMILY THROUGH THE AGES, BUT NOW, SADLY...

CURSED!

WHAT KIND OF CURSE, LADY ANGORA?

A DREADFUL CRUEL CURSE, OFFICER, STARTED BY MY GREAT-AUNT HERSELF.

CUCUMBER SANDWICHES AND A POT OF EARL GREY.

SHE HAUNTS IT!!!

ULP!

THERE IS A ROOM IN THE HOUSE CALLED *THE VELVET CHAMBER!*

HAUNTED BY THE GHOST OF MY GREAT-AUNT AND HER *THREE SPIRIT ENVOYS!*

THE CURSE STATES THAT IF A MAN OR WOMAN CAN SURVIVE A NIGHT IN THE ROOM, THE CURSE WILL BE LIFTED, AND THE HOUSE WILL BE FREE!

MANY HAVE TRIED...

BUT AS YET... NONE HAVE MANAGED...

ARRRRRRGH!!!

BUT LADY ANGORA—WHAT HAS HAPPENED TO THOSE WHO HAVE TRIED... AND FAILED??

OH OFFICERS! IT'S TOO DREADFUL.

WHATEVER ORDEAL THEY UNDERGO IN THE VELVET ROOM (AND OF COURSE NONE HAVE BEEN ABLE TO TELL)— THE SHOCK OF IT TURNS THEM...

TO ICE!!!

THE FOLLOWING DAY...

WELL THIS IS A NEW KIND OF CASE FOR US, SID!

I'M LOOKING FORWARD TO SOME FRESH COUNTRY AIR!

YOU CERTAINLY LOOK THE PART!

EVERYONE WEARS TWEED IN THE COUNTRYSIDE CHIEF! THIS WAY I'LL BLEND IN WITH THE LOCALS.

YES YOU'RE QUITE THE COUNTRY SQUIRE...

NOW, *THAT'S* STRANGE...

NOT AT ALL - IT'S A DEERSTALKER. A POPULAR COUNTRY HAT. SHERLOCK HOLMES WORE ONE.

NO, NOT YOUR HAT! OR, NOT JUST YOUR HAT- ACCORDING TO THIS MAP LADY ANGORA GAVE ME, ROUND THAT CORNER IS MOOR STREET.

SO?

SO, WE'RE IN THE MIDDLE OF ODDLEIGH...

NOWHERE NEAR THE COUNTRYSIDE!

HUH.

WELL I GUESS THAT'S LORRINGHAM, CHIEF.

NOT EXACTLY A CHEERY- LOOKING PILE IS IT.

MAYBE IT'S CHEERIER CLOSER UP! LAST ONE THERE IS A ROTTEN EGG!

EEP!

THAT MUST BE LADY ANGORA'S CAR.

DIDN'T SHE MENTION THAT HER BUTLER ACTUALLY LIVES HERE?

YEAH! IMAGINE WHO COULD BE BRAVE ENOUGH TO LIVE HERE ALL ALONE!

CREEEAAA

GREAT, OFFICERS- YOU FOUND US! AND I SEE YOU'VE MET ORSON!

DO COME IN!

WELCOME TO LORRINGHAM. THE MAP WAS OKAY?

YES IT WORKED A TREAT!

GOOD.

I THINK IT'S BEST IF I SHOW YOU AROUND STRAIGHT AWAY- NIGHT WILL SOON FALL.

THIS WAY, OFFICERS.

BY THE WAY, SERGEANT- GREAT DEERSTALKER!

TOLD YOU, CHIEF!

NOW BEFORE I OPEN THIS DOOR, OFFICERS, PLEASE BRACE YOURSELVES FOR A SHOCK.

DON'T WORRY, LADY ANGORA- WE'RE PROFESSIONALS.

BRR! IT'S SO COLD!!

GASP!!!

WHAT IS THIS??

THE CHILLER! WHERE WE KEEP ALL THOSE WHO TRIED- AND FAILED- TO BREAK THE CURSE. BRAVE, INNOCENT MEN AND WOMEN...

NOW NOTHING BUT POPSICLES!

ORSON AND I BROUGHT ALL THE AIR CONDITIONERS WE COULD FIND- TO KEEP THE ROOM COLD-

AND STOP THESE POOR PEOPLE MELTING...

BUT IT'S NOT ENOUGH!

THE SITUATION IS BECOMING CRITICAL...

UNLESS SOMEONE CAN SUCCESSFULLY SURVIVE A NIGHT IN THE VELVET ROOM,

AND BREAK THE CURSE SOON-

THESE PEOPLE WILL BE MERE PUDDLES ON THE FLOOR.

AND THIS, OFFICERS, IS THE VELVET CHAMBER.

CENTRE OF THE *APPALLING DANGER.*

AND YOUR ROOM FOR THE NIGHT!

AND HERE'S GREAT-AUNT GERTWIN HERSELF.

THE SOURCE OF ALL THE TROUBLE.

DISAPPOINTED BY LOVE IN HER YOUTH, SHE SWORE THAT IF SHE COULDN'T BE HAPPY, NEITHER WOULD HER DESCENDANTS... AND SHE'S MAKING SURE OF THAT!

ROTTEN OLD BAG!!!

MY LADY- NIGHT IS FALLING.

OH YES ORSON I'M COMING NOW!

I MUST AWAY, OFFICERS— BUT LET ME LEAVE YOU WITH ALL I KNOW... AS THE CLOCK STRIKES MIDNIGHT, SO BEGINS THE CURSE.

TO SURVIVE THE NIGHT YOU MUST PERFORM THREE TASKS, SET BY THREE VISITORS

FIRST

YOU MUST SOLVE THE RIDDLE OF THE CROW...

SECOND:

YOU MUST EMBRACE THE SPINY MAN...

AND THIRD:

YOU MUST CONSOLE THE WAILING WEASEL.

OH! GOOD LUCK, YOU POOR, BRAVE OFFICERS OF THE LAW!!!

HOW I WILL PRAY TO SEE YOUR WARM FACES COME MORNING!

AND NOT YOUR COLD, ICY FRAMES...

SAY, SID, DO YOU HEAR THAT SOUND?

KIND OF A SOBBING.

LIKE SOMEONE'S HEART IS BREAKING...

AND THEY CAN'T BE CONSOLED!

WELLL... THERE'S DEFINITELY SOMEONE CRYING IN THE FIREPLACE.

MISS, WHAT'S THE MATTER? WHY ARE YOU CRYING?

SHALL I PICK YOU UP FOR A CUDDLE?

WAAAAAAAAAAHAAA!

RECKON THAT'S A NO.

SID THIS IS THE WAILING WEASEL! WHAT SHALL WE DO?

I DON'T KNOW CHIEF!

LET'S THINK... WHAT MAKES US FEEL BETTER WHEN WE'RE SAD?

HMM GOOD QUESTION!

I LIKE... NOODLES, A NEW BOOK, SUNSHINE, GOOD NEWS,

A SMILE FROM THE CHIEF, A BIKE RIDE, MY TWEED COAT...

THE COLOUR GREEN, FRESH FLOWERS, A LETTER FROM DAD,

SAY SID, I DON'T WANT TO HURRY YOU, BUT-

GOOD GRIEF!!

WE HAVE TO FIND A WAY TO TURN THAT TAP OFF-AND FAST!

RIGHT. LET'S GET CHEERY ON THAT WEASEL.

HEY, DON'T CRY, MISS! UM- IT'S GOING TO BE SUNNY TOMORROW!

YOUR DRESS IS REALLY PRETTY!

NOTHING'S AS BAD AS IT SEEMS!

BUTTERFLIES EXIST!

EVERY CLOUD HAS A... UM- SILVER LINING!! I'M RUNNING OUT OF CHEERING THINGS, SID!

ARGH! ME TOO!

HEY! THERE'S DAD'S POETRY BOOK!

THAT'S ALWAYS COMFORTING!

TRY A FUNNY ONE, SID!

OKAY!

"AN ELDERLY MAN NAMED KEITH-"

"MISLAID HIS SET OF FALSE TEETH- THEY'D BEEN LAID ON A CHAIR"

"HE'D FORGOT THEY WERE THERE"

"HE SAT DOWN, AND WAS BITTEN BENEATH."

"BITTEN BENEATH..." HA HA

HA!

FLASH!

CHIEF! WE'VE CONSOLED THE WAILING WEASEL, HUGGED THE SPINY MAN AND SOLVED THE RIDDLE OF THE CROW!

COUGH

COUGH

D'YOU KNOW WHAT THAT MEANS??

ANOTHER CURSE BROKEN BY THE ODDLEIGH POLICE!

LET'S GO CALL LADY ANGORA!

BOY SID- I THOUGHT WE'D HAD IT FOR A MOMENT THERE!

ME TOO! AND I'M A PRETTY STRONG SWIMMER!

I CAN'T WAIT TO SEE THOSE PEOPLE ALL DEFROSTED AND SAFE!

RATTLE

WHY IS THE DOOR STILL LOCKED?? WE TOTALLY BROKE THAT CURSE!

I'VE GOT A BAD FEELING ABOUT THIS CHIEF...

THE END.

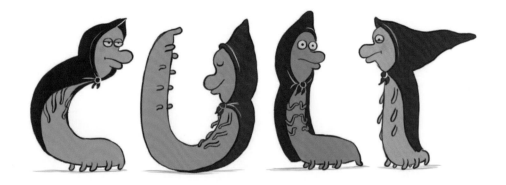

SO WHAT'S GOING ON HERE EXACTLY?

WE'RE CELEBRATING OUR NUMBER ONE'S BIRTH-DAY.

OH. A BIRTHDAY PARTY.

YES. TODAY OUR EXALTED LEADER HAS BEEN COCOONED FOR EXACTLY 100 DAYS.

HOW PATIENTLY WE'VE WAITED!

THIS IS A MOMENTOUS TIME. SOON HE WILL ECLOSE FROM HIS COCOON,

UNFURL HIS MIGHTY WINGS...

AND DESTROY YOU ALL!!!

CAKE?

SO WHAT'S THE BIG DEAL WITH YOUR LEADER BECOMING A BUTTERFLY? DON'T ALL YOU GUYS DO THAT?

THEORETICALLY, YES

BUT WHEN WE JOINED THE MISSION WE RENOUNCED OUR METAMORPHIC CAPABILITIES

HAD OUR HORMONAL SACS DEFIBRILLATED

ALL RIGHT REGGIE NO ONE WANTS TO HEAR THE DETAILS!

THAT SOUNDS PRETTY PAINFUL

BOY!! WAS IT!! YEEEE—OW!!!

OKAY, REGGIE!

PERFECTLY VOLUNTARY! ONLY BY REMAINING EARTHBOUND CAN WE TRULY GLORY IN OUR LEADER'S ASCENSION

WHIRRR WHIRRR

YE-OWW WWW!

REGGIE! THAT'S IT! GO TO THE THINKING ROOM!!

AND NO MORE CAKE FOR YOU!!

TELL ME, DID YOUR LEADER HAVE ANY ENEMIES?

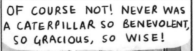

OF COURSE NOT! NEVER WAS A CATERPILLAR SO BENEVOLENT, SO GRACIOUS, SO WISE!

I MEAN, HE COULD BE A BIT LIGHT-FINGERED AND "STEAL-Y", IF YOU KNOW WHAT I'M SAYING...

YES...

BUT WHEN YOU'VE GOT THIS MANY HANDS YOU CAN'T KEEP TRACK OF WHAT <u>ALL</u> OF THEM ARE DOING!

TRUE DAT.

ANYWAY CHIEF, SURELY YOU AREN'T SUGGESTING *FOUL PLAY??*

I'M AFRAID WE CAN'T RULE ANYTHING OUT AT THIS STAGE. I BETTER INTERVIEW YOU ALL; ONE-BY-ONE.

OUR POOR LEADER!

LET'S START WITH YOUR MOVEMENTS THIS MORNING...

WELL, FIRST OF ALL I WOKE UP,

THEN I DID MY MORNING STRETCHING.

WE ALL ATE TOAST TOGETHER, AND

I WENT TO BUY BALLOONS FOR THE PARTY.

THEN WE CLEANED THE LEADER'S JAR

AND HAD SOME MORE TOAST, AND

AND THEN WE UH... WE UH...

...

ALRIGHT ALRIGHT I DID IT, IT WAS ME!! I'M SORRY!!!

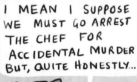

BLEURGH! ABOUT SEVEN MORE OF THESE AND I MIGHT GET THE TASTE OF CHRYSALIS OUT OF MY MOUTH!

WELL I GUESS THAT'S WHAT HAPPENS WHEN YOU GET MIXED UP WITH A CULT.

YOU'RE RIGHT, SID — BUT IT'S THE JOB. WE SPIED SUSPICIOUS ACTIVITY AND WE INVESTIGATED IT.

WE'RE THE THIN BLUE LINE IN THIS TOWN! WE SEE TROUBLE, AND—

BAM! WE'RE ON IT! LIKE RED ON A ROOSTER!

ANOTHER MILKSHAKE, CHIEF?

CHOCOLATE THIS TIME PLEASE!

Ptess
of the
Oddleigh Hills

THANK YOU FOR COMING SO QUICKLY, OFFICERS.

OF COURSE, PROFESSOR.

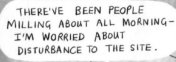

THERE'VE BEEN PEOPLE MILLING ABOUT ALL MORNING— I'M WORRIED ABOUT DISTURBANCE TO THE SITE.

THE POLICE TAPE SHOULD FIX THAT.

SO PROFESSOR, YOU WERE ALERTED TO THE DISCOVERY JUST THIS MORNING?

THAT'S RIGHT.

IT SEEMS THAT LAST NIGHT'S STORM CAUSED A SMALL LANDSLIDE —A JOGGER OUT FOR AN EARLY RUN CAME ACROSS IT!

LUCKILY SHE KNEW JUST WHO TO CALL— I CAME STRAIGHTAWAY. YOU CAN IMAGINE MY EMOTION WHEN I GOT HERE!

ABSOLUTELY!

I MEAN FOR A PALEONTOLOGIST, THIS IS CHRISTMAS, BIN DAY AND ALL MY BIRTHDAYS PUT TOGETHER!!!

SO IT'S A FOSSIL OF SOME KIND OF DINOSAUR, RIGHT?

OH, CHIEF! IT'S A PTERODACTYL!

THAT'S RIGHT OFFICER—A *PTERODACTYLUS*, LATE HETTANGIAN PERIOD.

A MOST STUNNING EXAMPLE!

WEREN'T YOU INTO DINOSAURS WHEN YOU WERE LITTLE, CHIEF?

NOT REALLY... I NEVER SAW THE APPEAL!

SHRUG

BUNCH OF BIG LIZARDS, LONG DEAD. (SORRY, PROFESSOR.)

NOT AT ALL.

CHIEF YOU'RE KILLING ME! I *LOVE* DINOSAURS!

OUR FEARSOME PRIMEVAL OVERLORDS! THE SIZE OF DOUBLE-DECKER BUSES - CRUNCHING UP TREES, TEARING UP MOUNTAINS GRRRR!

BRAVO! HEAR HEAR!

IT'S CERTAINLY A WONDERFUL MOMENT FOR DINOSAUR FANS!

SO WHAT'S NEXT, PROFESSOR?

I MUST CAREFULLY CLEAN AND PREPARE THE AREA!

DO NOT CROSS... DO NOT CROSS...

I HAVE MY FOSSIL-COLLECTING KIT HERE — HIGHLY SPECIALISED.

SO WE SEE!

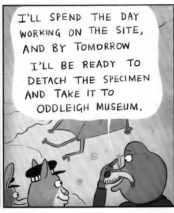

I'LL SPEND THE DAY WORKING ON THE SITE, AND BY TOMORROW I'LL BE READY TO DETACH THE SPECIMEN AND TAKE IT TO ODDLEIGH MUSEUM.

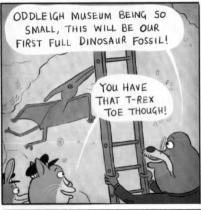

ODDLEIGH MUSEUM BEING SO SMALL, THIS WILL BE OUR FIRST FULL DINOSAUR FOSSIL!

YOU HAVE THAT T-REX TOE THOUGH!

YES! AND WE HAD THAT BRONTOSAURUS ELBOW — UNTIL IT TURNED OUT TO BE AN OLD COAT-HANGER

THAT WAS A BAD DAY FOR ODDLEIGH MUSEUM...

BUT THIS LITTLE BEAUTY'S GOING TO TURN *EVERYTHING* AROUND!

WELL THE BEACH IS QUIET AT LAST, SO WE'LL BE OFF NOW PROFESSOR — IT SEEMS YOU HAVE EVERYTHING IN HAND.

THANKS AGAIN OFFICERS!

HOPE YOU GET SOME SLEEP IN YOUR TENT!

HA! I'LL BE FINE — MUST GUARD THE SITE — GOODNIGHT!

WHAT A GREAT DAY EH CHIEF?

IT SURE WAS!

SEE YOU TOMORROW SID!

GOODNIGHT CHIEF!

DING-DONG!!

YAWN!

SID! IS IT MORNING ALREADY?

OKAY SID, LET'S CONSIDER THE FACTS.

A VALUABLE FOSSIL IS DISCOVERED IN THE ODDLEIGH CLIFF-FACE...

A PROFESSOR IS BIFFED ON THE HEAD WITH SOMETHING SHARP.

REALLY SHARP!

THE DOCTOR SAID IT WAS ALMOST LIKE HE'D BEEN PECKED BY A LARGE BIRD!

BIZARRE!

AND HAVING KNOCKED OUT THE PROFESSOR WITH SAID POINTED WEAPON...

THE THIEF ABSCONDS WITH THE FOSSIL!

SQUEEZE!

CRUNNCH!

SO, TO RECAP: WE'RE LOOKING FOR A RIVAL FOSSIL-COLLECTOR WITH A POINTED INSTRUMENT!

TO THE SCENE OF THE CRIME, SID!

OKAY, SID, YOU DUST THE ROCKFACE FOR PRINTS,

I'LL LOOK ROUND THE SURROUNDING AREA.

RIGHT YOU ARE CHIEF!

HMM...STRANGE TRACKS...

THEY SEEM TO END HERE!

SCREECH!

32

WELL I THINK PTESS IS OUR RESPONSIBILITY UNTIL THE PROFESSOR IS ON HIS FEET AGAIN.

GREAT! I'M GONNA FIND HER SOMETHING TO WEAR IN THE UNIFORM CUPBOARD.

CAW.

HERE WE GO!

LOOK, YOU'RE ONE OF US NOW!

CAW!

ME: SID! YOU: PTESS!

CAW.

CHIEF, IMAGINE! PTESS HAS BEEN IN THAT ROCK FOR OVER 65 MILLION YEARS! EVERYTHING HERE IS NEW TO HER!

SHE'S NEVER SEEN A FILM, OR RIDDEN A BIKE, OR TASTED A MILKSHAKE!

IN FACT... YOU KNOW WHAT NEEDS TO HAPPEN RIGHT NOW?

MODERN LIFE MONTAGE!!!

AND SO...

WITH GREAT POWER COMES GREAT RESPONSIBILITY...

PTESS! WHERE ARE YOU GOING??

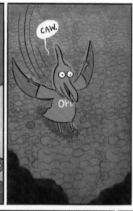

CAW.

CAW?

CAW!!!

CRAWW!

MARRRG!

OH! THANK GOODNESS!

CAW CAW CAW

ALTHOUGH NOW WE DO HAVE THREE DINOSAURS ON OUR HANDS!

I THINK WE SHOULD GO AND SEE THE PROFESSOR.

LOOK HOW HAPPY PTESS IS WITH HER MUM AND DAD. WHAT DO YOU THINK SHE'S SAYING TO THEM?

JUST TELLING THEM ABOUT THE GREAT POLICE OFFICERS SHE MET I GUESS!

HOW BRILLIANT AND CLEVER WE ARE!

HMM OKAY LET'S SAY IT'S THAT!

CAW CAW CAW!

The End

the

Dentist

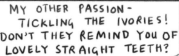

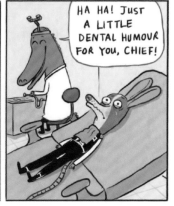

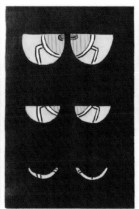

THE END

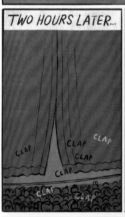

DID YOU ENJOY THE SHOW?

IT WAS MAGICAL!

GOOD GOOD.

THAT SONG ABOUT THE ORANGE ... AND THE ONE ABOUT HIS *FEELINGS*!

I KNOW.

HERE WE ARE. NOW, JUST TO WARN YOU, SOMETIMES HE'S A LITTLE TENSE AFTER A SHOW. *ARTISTIC TEMPERAMENT* AND ALL THAT!

FLYNN?

IT'S MAURIE.

FLYNN, I'VE BROUGHT THE TWO POLICE OFFICERS I TOLD YOU ABOUT.

FLYNN? GREAT SHOW, KID!

SO FLYNN, THESE ARE POLICE CHIEF JESSIE AND CONSTABLE SID.

I'VE ASKED THEM HERE TO OFFER ADVICE ON THE LITTLE PROBLEM WE'VE BEEN HAVING.

MAURIE...

MAURIE, I THOUGHT I'D MADE MYSELF VERY CLEAR ON THIS SUBJECT — *NO OUTSIDERS*!

I KNOW, FLYNN...

BUT MADDY INSISTED! SHE'S WORRIED ABOUT YOU!

UGH MAURIE — DO WHAT YOU WANT. BUT I'M TIRED OF THIS CONVERSATION.

WHY DON'T WE GO TO ANOTHER ROOM, OFFICERS, AND I CAN FILL YOU IN PROPERLY.

SORRY ABOUT THAT ... AS I SAID, HE'S NOT AT HIS BEST AFTER A SHOW — NORMALLY HE'S A GREAT GUY.

THIS SITUATION IS REALLY TAKING ITS TOLL...

THESE ARE THE LETTERS I TOLD YOU ABOUT.

ARE THEY ALL LIKE THIS?

OH YES.

PRETTY CHILLING, AREN'T THEY?

WELL...

FLYNn you STINKO you CHeW FooD Like a MaD STegOsAuR

I MEAN, THEY'RE ANNOYING, CERTAINLY— BUT ARE THEY A POLICE MATTER?

WELL THERE'S MORE TO IT, OFFICER.

IN OSLO SOMEONE PUT HONEY ON HIS GUITAR STRINGS, AND IN TORONTO WE FOUND A WHOOPEE CUSHION ON HIS PIANO STOOL!

AND, WHEN WE GOT TO ATLANTA,

FLYNN DISCOVERED THAT SOMEONE HAD PUT CHEWING GUM IN HIS FAVOURITE HAIRBRUSH! NOW, PERHAPS NOTHING FATAL HAS HAPPENED BUT HIS SISTER INSISTED I CALL YOU, AND GIVEN BOTH SHE AND FLYNN ARE SO FAMOUS...

WELL, HERE YOU ARE.

YOU UNDER-STAND.

SO YOU'RE SAYING THAT BECAUSE HE'S FAMOUS HE DESERVES SPECIAL TREATMENT.

YOU GOT IT!

URGH, CELEBRITIES! I MEAN, A WORM IN HIS CEREAL?! PLEASE!

SO WHAT DO WE DO, CHIEF? DO WE GET INVOLVED?

I DON'T KNOW... I GUESS SOME OF THE LETTERS WERE A LITTLE STRANGE.

GRUMBLE.

LOOK, CHIEF—

THE WHOLE FAMILY.

THE CARRINGTONS

THE POOR GUY'S BEEN FAMOUS HIS WHOLE LIFE! HE NEVER EVEN HAD A CHOICE.

MAYBE IT'S NOT SURPRISING HE'S KIND OF... PRICKLY.

IMAGINE NOT BEING ABLE TO CHOOSE TO BE A POLICE OFFICER, CHIEF!

PERISH THE THOUGHT, SID!

OKAY FINE, LET'S GO TALK TO FLYNN AND SEE WHAT WE CAN WORK OUT.

WE ONLY HAVE TO KEEP AN EYE ON HIM AND FIGURE OUT WHO'S SENDING THE LETTERS.

NO PROBLEM FOR US, CHIEF!

MR. CARRINGTON? POLICE AGAIN— MAY WE COME IN?

OH! SORRY! WE DIDN'T KNOW YOU HAD COMPANY.

I HAVEN'T. THIS IS MY SISTER.

CHARMING.

WELL COME ON FLYNN, INTRODUCE ME TO THE NICE POLICE OFFICERS.

OH PLEASE.

YOU'LL HAVE TO DO IT YOURSELF. I REALLY CAN'T BE EXPECTED TO REMEMBER THE NAMES OF EVERY PASSING COPPER.

IGNORE MY BROTHER, OFFICERS. HE WAS BORN DISAGREEABLE. I'M MADDY CARRINGTON.

I KNOW YOU ARE!

I HAD SEVEN POSTERS OF YOU IN MY BEDROOM WHEN I WAS GROWING UP!!!

MR CARRINGTON YOU'VE MADE IT QUITE PLAIN YOU DON'T WANT US HERE. BUT BOTH YOUR SISTER AND MANAGER THINK YOU'RE IN DANGER.

SO THOUGH YOU MAY LIKE IT AS LITTLE AS I DO— WE'RE STICKING TO YOU FOR NOW.

UGH, FINE!

OH, GOODY!

DON'T BE CROSS FLYNN, IT'S ONLY NATURAL FOR ME TO WORRY ABOUT MY LITTLE BRO!

PINCH!

UGH, GET OFF MADDY!

I KNOW THIS IS AWKWARD CHIEF BUT YOU'VE MADE THE RIGHT DECISION.

I THINK SO TOO SID.

WHY CAN'T YOU EVER MIND YOUR OWN BUSINESS!!

JUST THINK WHAT AN INCENTIVE THIS'LL BE TO FIND THE LETTER-WRITER QUICKLY!

HA! TRUE.

MADDY YOU HOTDOG!

YOU'RE THE HOTDOG.

PLUS HOW BAD CAN IT REALLY BE?

THAT'S THE SPIRIT, CHIEF!

GET OFF ME, ELEPHANT BUM!!

WHY, IS THIS FLYNN CARRINGTON I SEE BEFORE ME?!

HI GERRY!

NICE TO SEE YOU FLYNN! IT'S BEEN A WHILE. STILL A SIZE EIGHT?

HA HA YEAH! GOOD MEMORY, THANKS GERRY.

AND WHAT ABOUT YOUR FRIEND? WHAT SIZE FEET ARE YOU, MISS?

OH!

NO THANKS, I'M JUST HERE TO WATCH!

THERE ARE NO BYSTANDERS AT GERRY'S WORLD OF ICE! NOW, WHAT SIZE?

OH! UH, SIX I GUESS.

VOILA!

GERRY SEEMS NICE.

YEAH HE'S GREAT. I COME HERE WHENEVER I'M IN ODDLEIGH.

THERE AREN'T THAT MANY PLACES I CAN COME AND JUST BE ME.

FLYNN THE PERSON, NOT THE PERFORMER.

AND BE FREE!

YARRRGH!

CHIEF!

ARE YOU OKAY? THAT LOOKED BAD!

HA, OH I'M OKAY.

THANK YOU!

JUST — SOME JOKER SEEMS TO HAVE COVERED THIS FLOOR IN ICE.

HA! SO, YOU'RE NOT MUCH OF A SKATER I GUESS?

WELL — THIS IS MY FIRST TIME TRYING IT!

OH!

I WISH I HAD YOUR FLAIR!

OH. WELL, JUST ANOTHER LEGACY FROM CARRINGTON FAMILY SINGERS... MUST HAVE ALL THE ACCOMPLISHMENTS.

YOU SOUND SO BITTER.

I'D LOVE TO HAVE YOUR GIFTS.

I KNOW WHAT I SOUND LIKE— AND WHAT YOU MUST THINK OF ME.

BUT MADDY AND I WERE BORN INTO THE BAND, NO-ONE ASKED US WHAT WE WANTED.

AND NOW IT'S HARD FOR US TO TRUST OTHER PEOPLE.

YOU SEEM TO TRUST MAURIE.

OH WELL HE'S PART OF THE FAMILY.

ISN'T THAT FLYNN CARRINGTON??

...

I'M SORRY I WAS RUDE TO YOU BEFORE.

OH. THAT'S OKAY.

YOU KNOW, I COME FROM A DYNASTY TOO— MY FAMILY ARE ALL IN THE POLICE!

REALLY?

YEAH. BUT MY MUM WAS KEENER I LEARN TO WRESTLE THAN TO ICE SKATE!

WELL YOU'RE DOING A PRETTY GOOD JOB RIGHT NOW!

?

SEE?

OH YEAH!!!

YES I SEE — YOU'RE CERTAIN, ARE YOU? OKAY, THANK YOU FAYE.

PSSST CHIEF!

CHIEF

CHIEF!

CHIEF.

CHIEF.

CHIEF.

CHIEEEF!!

I BETTER GO— THANKS FOR THE SKATE.

ANYTIME.

SORRY SID, I WAS JUST, UH...

WEIRD NEWS, CHIEF.

I SENT SOME LETTERS TO FINGERPRINT FAYE AND SHE'S JUST COME BACK TO ME...

SHE FOUND TRACES OF FLYNN'S PRINTS, NATURALLY HE HANDLED THE LETTERS WHEN HE READ THEM...

BUT THE ONLY OTHER PRINTS WERE SO SIMILAR TO FLYNN'S, THAT...

FAYE SAID THEY COULD ONLY HAVE COME FROM...

TELL ME TELL ME!!

FLYNN'S SIBLING!

GASP!

YOU MEAN...

MADDY!!!

SLAM

?

The End

ODDLEIGH ORACLE
CROSSWORD

ACROSS

2. A friend in _____ is a friend indeed (5)
6. The caterpillar who isn't allowed any more cake (6)
7. The three letters on the t-shirt Sid puts Ptess into (3)
8. An elderly man who mislaid his set of false teeth (5)
9. Which film do Sid, Jessie and Ptess see? (9)
12. Ptess's favourite word (3)
13. The _____ Family Singers (10)
18. What does the professor's Brontosaurus bone turn out to be? (4,7)
19. What does Great-Aunt Gertwin's curse turn people to? (3)

DOWN

1. The _____ Chamber is haunted (6)
3. A tooth which is also a dentist (7)
4. A stately home (10)
5. What kind of hides does Sid say they'd need to hug the Spiny Man? (9)
9. The symbol on Flynn's dressing room door (4)
10. A type of country hat, also worn by Sherlock Holmes (11)
11. A dried fruit in the jar where the Number One should be (5)
14. The number of days the exulted leader had been cocooned for (3)
15. The answer to the final crossword clue in Haunting of Lorringham (6)
16. The colour of Dr Incisor's uniform (5)
17. Type of animal that Maurie is (4)

FLYNN YOU STINKO YOU CHEW FOOD LIKE a MAD STEGOSAUR

EVIDENCE

Lorrugham

SPINES FROM "SPINY MAN"

ODDLEIGH POLICE DEPT

Cocoonies Hall

EVIDENCE

DENTIST

"PAPA" MOLAR

PTERODACTYLUS

ODDLEIGH POLICE DEPARTMENT

Great-Aunt Gertwin

An elderly man named Keith,
Mislaid his set of false teeth.
They'd been placed on a chair,
He'd forgot they were there,
He sat down, and was bitten beneath.

If You Were a Pebble

by Sid Senior

If you were a pebble,
a pebble on the beach,
I would be the wave that lapped
and kept you within reach.

And if you were a ship
a-blowing on the storm,
I would be the harbour
to keep you safe and warm.

If you were a shiny star,
Far off in the night
I would be the telescope
that kept you in my sight.

And if you were an apple
growing on the tree,
I would be the basket
that took you home with me.

If you were a little moth
flutt'ring in the night,
I would be the candle
that drew you to the light.

If you were a teapot
and you were full of tea,
I would be the cosy
so's to keep you close to me.

If you were a picture
hanging on the wall
I would be the picture frame
that would not let you fall.

And if you were a storybook
waiting to be read,
I would pick you from the shelf
and take you up to bed.

But you are my little one
Good and kind and bright
And I have lips to kiss your face
And arms to hold you tight.

Good night!

Glossary and Notes on the Text

The Haunting of Lorringham

Pg 7
Silhouette of Sherlock Holmes, demonstrating his
fondness for the deerstalker, illustrated to the right.

Pg 10
Sid reads from "*If You Were a Pebble*", written by his dad, Sid Snr.

Pg 14
Sid reads a limerick by the prolific author, Anonymous.

Cult

Pg 20
Eclose: *verb*: ENTOMOLOGY (of an insect) emerge as an adult
from the pupa or as a larva from the egg.

Pg 20
It is unknown where the hormonal sacs of these caterpillars are located,
or what defibrillation might entail. But it might require a comb.

Pg 21
Everyone knows that hairy caterpillars will sting you with their hair.

Pg 21
Cell Soup - First, the caterpillar digests itself, releasing enzymes to dissolve
all of its tissues. If you were to cut open a cocoon or chrysalis at just the right time,
caterpillar soup would ooze out. But the contents of the pupa are not
entirely an amorphous mess. Certain highly organized groups of cells
known as imaginal discs survive the digestive process.
Before hatching, when a caterpillar is still developing inside its egg,
it grows an imaginal disc for each of the adult body parts it will need
as a mature butterfly or moth—discs for its eyes, for its wings,
its legs and so on.
In some species, these imaginal discs remain dormant throughout
the caterpillar's life; in other species, the discs begin to take the
shape of adult body parts even before the caterpillar forms a
chrysalis or cocoon. Some caterpillars walk around with tiny
rudimentary wings tucked inside their bodies, though you would
neve⸏⸏ ⸏ it by looking at them.
F⸏⸏⸏⸏⸏ (August 10, 2012) "How Does a Caterpillar Turn into a Butterfly?"
⸏⸏⸏⸏ *⸏ican.*

⸏⸏⸏⸏⸏ ⸏ormally made of poop.

Ptess of the Oddleigh Hills

Pg 29
"The size of double-decker buses..." – absence of double-decker buses
in the Hettangian Period makes Sid's claim here hard to verify.

Pg 37
Professor Cuvier:
Jean Léopold Nicolas Frédéric, Baron Cuvier; (23 August 1769 – 13 May 1832),
known as Georges Cuvier, was a French naturalist and zoologist,
sometimes referred to as the "founding father of paleontology".
Cuvier was a major figure in natural sciences research in the
early 19th century and was instrumental in establishing the fields
of comparative anatomy and paleontology through his work in comparing
living animals with fossils.
Wikipedia.

The Dentist

Pg 44
Dr Incisor's current marital status is unknown.

The Bodyguards

Pg 53
Chief Inspector Jessie's family are all notable police officers,
and her cousin Superintendent Fred was recently awarded a
blue ribbon for Gallantry in the Face of Extreme Weirdness.

CROSSWORD ANSWERS

ACROSS
2. Tweed
6. Reggie
7. OPD
8. Keith
9. Spiderman
12. Caw
13. Carrington
18. Coat hanger
19. Ice

DOWN
1. Velvet
3. Incisor
4. Lorringham
5. Elephant
9. Star
10. Deerstalker
11. Prune
14. 100
15. Bottom
16. White
17. Toad

TOR FREEMAN

HAS BEEN WRITING AND ILLUSTRATING
BOOKS FOR CHILDREN SINCE 1999.

HER BOOKS INCLUDE
SHOWTIME FOR BILLIE AND COCO,
THE DIGBY DOG AND OLIVE SERIES,
AND THE TOUCAN BROTHERS.

IN 2013 SHE WAS AWARDED
A SENDAK FELLOWSHIP AND
IN 2017 SHE WAS THE
WINNER OF THE OBSERVER/CAPE/COMICA
SHORT GRAPHIC STORY PRIZE.

THIS IS HER FIRST
PUBLISHED COMIC BOOK.

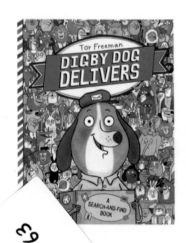

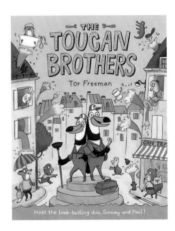

www.torfreeman.com